Sh
G000111903

# TWELFTH NIGHT

*A shortened and simplified version
in modern English*

by

John & Leela Hort

THE KABET PRESS
1985

For Peter, Michael and Patrick

# CONTENTS

The play takes place in a city in Illyria and on the sea coast nearby

# PEOPLE IN THE PLAY

| | |
|---|---|
| **Duke (or Count) Orsino** | The Duke of Illyria. He is in love with Lady Olivia. |
| **Lady (or Countess) Olivia** | A rich countess, whose brother has recently died. |
| **Curio** <br> **Valentine** } | Two of the Duke's attendants. |
| **Sir Toby Belch** | Lady Olivia's uncle. He lives in her house. |
| **Sir Andrew Aguecheek** | A friend of Sir Toby Belch. He wants to marry Lady Olivia. |
| **Malvolio** | Lady Olivia's steward. He manages her household. |
| **Maria** | Lady Olivia's maid. She is as much a companion as a servant. |
| **Viola** | A young lady who disguises herself as a man and calls herself Cesario. Later she is mistaken for her brother. |
| **Sebastian** | Viola's twin brother. |
| **Captain** | The captain of the ship in which Viola and Sebastian were travelling when they were shipwrecked. |
| **Antonio** | Another ship's captain. He rescued Sebastian and became his friend. |
| **Clown** | A jester, one of Lady Olivia's servants. His name is Feste. |
| **Fabian** | Another of Lady Olivia's servants. |

**Attendants, sailors, musicians, two policemen, a priest.**


Pronunciation of names:

        Orsino: "orseeno"
        Curio: Curi as in "curious", then o as in "old"
        Aguecheek: Ag as in "vague", but ue as in "cue"
        Cesario: "see zario"
        Illyria: To rhyme with "Syria"


Characters who appear in a scene are given in a box at the beginning of the scene.
Non-speaking parts are in brackets.

# ACT ONE

## SCENE 1

A room in Duke Orsino's palace

> Duke
> Curio
> Valentine
> (Musicians)
> (Attendants)

*[**Musicians** are playing and the **Duke** is listening.
**Curio** and some **Attendants** are with him]*

**Duke** *[When the music stops]* Play on! *[The music starts again]* Oh, that haunting melody! It reminds me of spring time and spring flowers...*[He listens for a while]* But stop, that's enough: it doesn't sound so sweet any more. *[The music stops]* Oh Curio, love makes everything else seem unimportant.

**Curio** Why not go hunting, my lord?

**Duke** But I do, for my love! Ever since I first saw the lovely Olivia I have been tormented by my love for her. *[**Valentine** comes in]* Ah, what does she say?

**Valentine** They wouldn't let me see her, sir, but I did speak to her maid. The Lady Olivia has decided to live like a nun for seven years, in mourning for her brother.

**Duke** A woman who can show such feeling for a dead brother will surely make a loving wife. Come! Let's go into the gardens and there, among the sweet flowers, dream of love.

## SCENE 2

The coast of Illyria

> Viola
> Captain
> (Sailors)

*[**Viola**, a ship's **Captain** and some **Sailors** come in. Their clothes are wet and torn]*

**Viola** Where are we?

**Captain** In Illyria, madam.

**Viola** But my poor brother is in heaven! Or do you think he could still be alive?

**Captain** Well, it is possible, madam. After our ship went down, and you and a few others were saved, I saw your brother tie himself to a broken mast that was floating on the sea.

1

**Viola** Oh, thank you, Captain, you have given me new hope. And if *I* managed to escape, why shouldn't *he?* [*Pause*] Do you know this country?

**Captain** Yes, madam, I know it well. I was born and brought up near here.

**Viola** Who is the governor?

**Captain** A noble Duke, called Orsino.

**Viola** Orsino! I've heard my father talk about him. Is he still a bachelor?

**Captain** Yes, madam, as far as I know. But they say that he wants to marry the Lady Olivia.

**Viola** Who is she?

**Captain** The daughter of a Count, who died a year ago, leaving her in the care of her brother. But soon afterwards he died too. She is heartbroken, and has decided to shut herself away from the world.

**Viola** I would like to work for such a lady. That would give me time to consider what to do next.

**Captain** I'm afraid that would be rather difficult. She won't see anyone, not even the Duke.

**Viola** Captain, you look honest, and I'm sure I can trust you. Please get me some men's clothes, so that I can disguise myself and become a servant to this Duke. I'll be able to entertain him: I can sing and play. And I'll call myself "Cesario". But you must keep my secret.

**Captain** Madam, I'll do my best.


### SCENE 3
The kitchen in Lady Olivia's house

| Sir Toby |
|---|
| Maria |
| Sir Andrew |

[*Sir Toby Belch and Maria come in*]

**Sir Toby** Why the hell does my niece have to go on being so miserable about her brother's death? Worry is bad for you.

**Maria** Look here, Sir Toby, you've got to stop coming in so late at night. My lady has had enough of it.

**Sir Toby** I don't care!

**Maria** But you must learn to fit in better.

**Sir Toby** So long as I can fit into my coat and boots, and get tight in them, I'm happy.

**Maria** All that drinking you do will ruin you. My lady was talking about it only the other night, and about that stupid knight who wants to marry her.

**Sir Toby** Sir Andrew Aguecheek?

2

**Maria** Yes.

**Sir Toby** [*Proudly*] He's the bravest man in Illyria.

**Maria** So what?

**Sir Toby** So he has thirty thousand pounds a year.

**Maria** A fool and his money are soon parted.

**Sir Toby** Nonsense! He's a musician, and he knows three or four languages. What's more, he knows them by heart! He's a genius!

**Maria** Yes, he's a genius at quarrelling. And they say that if he wasn't such a good coward, he'd be dead by now.

**Sir Toby** The lying rascals! Who are they?

**Maria** And they say he gets drunk with you every night.

**Sir Toby** Yes, but he drinks to my niece. And I'll drink to her too, so long as there's a hole in my throat and beer in Illyria! Anyone who doesn't drink to her is a coward. Ah! Here *is* Sir Andrew Agueface.

[*Sir Andrew Aguecheek comes in*]

**Sir Andrew** Hullo, Sir Toby Belch. [*To Maria*] Good morning, little mouse.

**Maria** The same to you, sir!

**Sir Toby** Confront her, Sir Andrew!

**Sir Andrew** W-what's that?

**Sir Toby** She's my niece's maid.

**Sir Andrew** Oh! [*To Maria*] How do you do, Miss Confront?

**Sir Toby** Idiot! I mean, get to work! Flatter her, win her heart!

**Sir Andrew** Oh, is *that* what "confront" means?

**Maria** Goodbye, gentlemen. [*She starts to go away*]

**Sir Toby** Quick, Sir Andrew! If you let her escape, you're a coward.

**Sir Andrew** [*Very worried, to Maria*] He says that if I let you escape, I'm a coward. [*Maria laughs*] Do you take us for fools?

**Maria** I wouldn't take *you* anywhere! [*She goes out*]

**Sir Andrew** I think all that beef I eat hurts my brains.

**Sir Toby** Of course it does.

**Sir Andrew** Do you really think so? I'd better go home tomorrow.

**Sir Toby** *Pourquoi,* dear knight?

**Sir Andrew** What does that mean? "To go" or "not to go"? Oh, I wish I'd spent more time on languages instead of going to parties.

**Sir Toby** That would have made your hair curl.

**Sir Andrew** Really? Doesn't it suit me like this?

**Sir Toby** Mmm...let's have a look. It would make a good mop for a housewife.

**Sir Andrew** [*Miserably*] Anyway the Count wants to marry your niece.

3

**Sir Toby** Don't worry, Sir Andrew, she won't marry the Count. She doesn't want anyone older, richer or cleverer than herself. You've got a good chance.

**Sir Andrew** All right, I'll stay another month. Anyway, I *adore* parties.

**Sir Toby** Can you dance, knight?

**Sir Andrew** Of course I can. I'm the best dancer in the country—except for the chaps who are better than me.

**Sir Toby** Why didn't you tell me so before? You should rock to church and roll back again! You shouldn't hide your talents. [*Sir Andrew starts dancing*] You've got a fine pair of legs!

**Sir Andrew** Not bad, not bad. Shall we arrange a dance?

**Sir Toby** Yes, let's. That's right! [*He claps his hands to encourage Sir Andrew*] Come on, faster! That's the way. [*They dance out*]

SCENE 4

A room in the Duke's palace

| Valentine |
| --- |
| Viola (disguised as Cesario) |
| Duke |
| (Curio) |
| (Attendants) |

[*Valentine comes in, with Viola dressed as a man*]

**Valentine** If the Duke goes on being so kind to you, Cesario, you'll go far.

**Viola** Why "if"? Does he often change his mind about people?

**Valentine** No....

**Viola** I'm glad about th—. Oh! Here he comes.

[*The Duke comes in with Curio and some Attendants*]

**Duke** Ah, there you are, Cesario. [*To Curio and the Attendants*] Leave us. [*They go to the back of the stage*] Cesario, I have told you all my secrets. You *must* see her.

**Viola** But my lord, she's in mourning. I'm sure she won't ——

**Duke** Forget about manners. Insist on seeing her.

**Viola** Supposing she *does* see me, what then?

**Duke** Tell her how much I love her. She's more likely to listen to you than to an older man.

**Viola** To me?

**Duke** Yes, she'll like you because you're young and attractive. I'm sure you'll succeed. And I'll reward you well. [*To his Attendants*] Go with him. I want to be alone.

4

**Viola** I'll do my best to win her for you, my lord. [*The Duke goes out with Curio, and Viola speaks to the audience*] What a hopeless situation! You see, I'd give anything to be his wife myself!

SCENE 5

A room in Lady Olivia's House

| Maria |
| Clown |
| Olivia |
| (Attendants) |
| Malvolio |
| Sir Toby |
| Viola |

[*Maria and the Clown come in*]

**Maria** Where have you been hiding? You'd better tell me, or I won't make any more excuses for you. My lady is going to have you hanged.

**Clown** I don't mind if she hangs me. I'll be out of trouble then. Anyway, many a good hanging has stopped a bad marriage.

**Maria** Or you may lose your job.

**Clown** I'd rather lose my job than lose my trousers. Especially with you around.

**Maria** That's enough from you! Ah, here comes my lady. You'd better think of a good excuse. [*She goes out*]

**Clown** I think I'd better try and amuse her. At least I know I'm not clever. That's better than thinking you are and then making a fool of yourself. [*Olivia and Malvolio come in with some Attendants*] God bless you, lady!

**Olivia** Take the fool away. He's not funny, and he's dishonest.

**Clown** Beer and good advice will soon cure those faults, madam. Give the fool a drink and he'll go all funny. Give a dishonest man some good advice and he'll mend his ways. Or if he can't mend them himself, he can always send for the counsel. [*To an Attendant*] Well, do as you're told, man! Take the lady away.

**Olivia** Sir, I told them to take *you* away.

**Clown** May I prove that you're a fool, madam?

**Olivia** Very well, if you can.

**Clown** Madam, why are you in mourning?

**Olivia** Because my brother is dead.

**Clown** I think his soul is in hell.

**Olivia** I *know* it is in heaven.

**Clown** Then you *are* a fool, mourning for a soul that is in heaven. [*To the Attendant*] Take the fool away.

5

**Olivia** Don't you think he's improving, Malvolio?

**Malvolio** That shouldn't be difficult for him. Every fool gets sillier as he gets older.

**Clown** In that case, sir, may *you* grow old quickly! Sir Toby knows I'm not wise, but he's not sure that you're no fool.

**Olivia** What do you say to that, Malvolio?

**Malvolio** [*Haughtily*] I'm surprised your ladyship finds the rascal amusing. I saw an ordinary fool outwit him the other day. And look at him now, he's run out of jokes already.

**Olivia** You are too conceited, Malvolio, and you take life much too seriously. Surely a jester may joke, just as a steward may scold.

**Clown** Well said, lady!

[*Maria comes in again*]

**Maria** Madam, there is a young gentleman at the gate who wants to see you.

**Olivia** From Count Orsino?

**Maria** I don't know, madam, but he's a handsome young man. Sir Toby is talking to him.

**Olivia** That madman! Get Toby away, Maria. [*Maria goes out*] Malvolio, if this gentleman has come from the Count, get rid of him. Tell him I'm ill, or not at home, whatever you like. [*Malvolio goes out. Olivia speaks to the Clown*] You need to be careful, sir. People are beginning to dislike your fooling.

**Clown** Thank you for speaking up for us fools just now, ma'am. Anyone would think you had a son in the business yourself. Ah! Here comes your weak-brained cousin.

[*Sir Toby comes in drunk*]

**Olivia** Good lord, half drunk! Who is the man at the gate, cousin?

**Sir Toby** A gentle gentleman who— [*He belches*] Damn those pickled herrings! Hi, fool!

**Clown** Hi, Sir Toby.

**Olivia** What a time to be drunk!

**Sir Toby** Who called me a punk? Someone at the gate— hic!

**Olivia** Who is it?

**Sir Toby** Could be the devil himself for all I care! [*He goes out*]

**Olivia** What's a drunken man like, fool?

**Clown** That depends, madam. One drink too many makes a man a fool, the second makes him mad, and the third one drowns him.

**Olivia** Then go and find an undertaker. My cousin is drowned.

**Clown** Sir Toby is only at the mad stage my lady. And a fool can look after a madman. [*He goes out*]

6

[*Malvolio comes in again*]

**Malvolio** This young fellow is *determined* to see you, madam. I told him you were ill, but he said that was why he wanted to speak to you. Then I told him you were asleep, and he said *that* was why he wanted to see you. What shall I say to him, madam? He won't take "no" for an answer.

**Olivia** Tell him I will *not* see him.

**Malvolio** I *have* told him, madam, but he says he will stand at your gate like a wooden post until you do.

**Olivia** What is he like?

**Malvolio** [*He sniffs*] Rather unpleasant.

**Olivia** Describe him. How old is he?

**Malvolio** He looks no more than a teenager to me. He's very handsome, but he's a cheeky fellow.

**Olivia** [*After thinking for a moment*] Show him in. [*Malvolio starts going*] Call Maria.

**Malvolio** [*He calls as he goes out*] Maria!

[*Maria comes in again*]

**Olivia** Maria, my veil. I'll hear Orsino's case once more.

[*Viola comes in*]

**Viola** Which is the lady of the house?

**Olivia** I will answer for her.

**Viola** "O most lovely lady..." [*She pauses*] Are you *really* the lady of the house? I don't want to waste my fine speech on the wrong person. [*She looks from Olivia to Maria and back again*] Sweet ladies, please don't tease me.

**Olivia** Where have you come from?

**Viola** There's nothing about *that* in my speech.

**Olivia** Are you an actor?

**Viola** Of course not. *That's* not my game. But please, are you the lady of the house?

**Olivia** I am.

**Viola** Good. Now for my speech. Let me see: first I must praise your beauty, then give the important part of my message.

**Olivia** You can leave out the praise.

**Viola** But I spent *hours* learning it, and it's ever so poetic.

**Olivia** And insincere, I have no doubt. Come, sir! I only allowed you in out of curiosity. If you have anything sensible to say, say it. If not, go.

**Maria** [*Pointing to the door*] Why don't you head for the open sea, sir?

7

**Viola** [*To Maria*] Thank you, sailor, but I'll stay in port a little longer. [*To Olivia*] Please give your deckhand a tot of rum, lady, to keep her quiet... What message shall I take to the Duke?

**Olivia** What's all this fuss about? Anyone would think you were here on some really serious business! Ah well, let's hear your message.

**Viola** It is secret, and for your ears only, madam.

**Olivia** Very well, I'll listen to this secret. [*To Maria and the Attendants*] Leave us. [*They go out*] Well?

**Viola** "Lovely lady..."

**Olivia** Yes, very nice. But what about the message?

**Viola** It is from Orsino.

**Olivia** What does he say?

**Viola** That he loves you.

**Olivia** Is that all?

**Viola** [*After a pause*] Madam, may I see your face?

**Olivia** What has my face got to do with your message? But never mind, [*she lifts her veil*] I'll show you the picture. Don't you think it's well done?

**Viola** Very fine, if it's not out of a paint box!

**Olivia** I promise you it won't wash off.

**Viola** It would be wicked not to pass on such beauty to a child.

**Olivia** Don't worry, I'll list the bits and pieces in my will. Item one: two lips, reddish; item two: two grey eyes with lids; one neck, one chin, and so on.

**Viola** Oh, you are proud! But there's no denying your beauty. And my master loves you passionately.

**Olivia** I know he is noble, handsome and rich, but I cannot love him, and he knows it.

**Viola** If I loved you as truly as my master does, your refusal wouldn't make sense. I wouldn't understand it.

**Olivia** Why, what would you do?

**Viola** I would live by your gate in a little hut and write poems and sing them aloud all night. I would make the hills echo with your name until you took pity on me.

**Olivia** [*Thoughtfully*] You might succeed. Who *are* you?

**Viola** More than I seem. I am a gentleman.

**Olivia** Go back to your master, and tell him that I cannot love him. [*Softly*] But if you like *you* may come and tell me how he takes my refusal. [*She offers her a purse*] I want you to have this. Goodbye.

**Viola** [*She does not take the purse*] I don't need tipping, madam. It is my master who needs your kindness, not me. And I hope you will be as unlucky in love as my poor master. Goodbye, cruel lady. [*She goes out*]

**Olivia** "More than I seem. I am a gentleman." He's the finest I ever saw! Oh, what am I saying? Can I be—? If only he were Orsino! Can one fall in love so quickly? [*She calls*] Malvolio! [*She sighs, and takes off a ring*] Ah well!

[*Malvolio comes in*]

**Malvolio** Yes, madam?

**Olivia** Run after that bad tempered messenger and give this ring back to him. [*She gives him the ring*] Tell him I won't have it. And he needn't raise the Count's hopes either. I will never marry Orsino. But if the youth comes again tomorrow, I will explain why. Quick, Malvolio!

**Malvolio** Yes, madam. [*He hurries out*]

**Olivia** What *am* I doing? Ah well, what will be will be.

9

# ACT TWO

## SCENE 1
### At the door of Antonio's house

[*Antonio* and **Sebastian** *come in*]

> Antonio
> Sebastian

**Antonio** Must you go? Won't you let me come with you?

**Sebastian** No, Antonio, no. I've had a lot of bad luck lately, and I may be heading for more trouble. I'd hate you to get involved, so I think I'd better go alone.

**Antonio** At least tell me where you are going.

**Sebastian** Oh, I'm just going to wander about. [*Pause*] Antonio, I can see that you want to know more about me, but you are too polite to ask. Well, I'll tell you. I am Sebastian, the son of Sebastian of Messaline; I'm sure you've heard of my father. I had a twin sister, a lovely girl, who was drowned a few hours before you rescued me. [*He sighs*] Oh, I wish I had drowned with her.

**Antonio** Can't I at least come with you as your servant?

**Sebastian** I'm afraid I must say "no", though I hate doing it. I am going to Count Orsino's court. Goodbye. [*He goes out*]

**Antonio** Goodbye. [*To himself*] I've got enemies in Orsino's court, but I am so fond of you that I will follow you.


## SCENE 2
### A street near Lady Olivia's house

[*Viola comes in, and then **Malvolio** hurries in after her*]

> Malvolio
> Viola

**Malvolio** You were with the Countess Olivia just now, weren't you?

**Viola** Yes, sir.

**Malvolio** Here's your ring. You could have saved me the bother by taking it away yourself. My lady says she will never marry your master, and you are not to bring any more messages from him. But if you like, you can come back and tell her how he takes her refusal. Here you are. [*He tries to give her the ring*]

10

**Viola** [*She does not take the ring*] But she took it from me. I don't want it.

**Malvolio** She says you threw it to her in a temper, and she wants me to return it. There you are! [*He throws the ring on the ground*] You can take it or leave it. [*He goes out*]

**Viola** This is strange, I didn't leave a ring with her. What can it mean? [*She picks up the ring and looks at it*] I wonder if she has fallen in love with me, because of my disguise? Yes, the way she looked at me... Poor thing, I'm afraid she has, and this is her way of telling me. How easily we women fall for a handsome face! [*She sighs*] What a situation! My master loves her, I love him, and she loves me. Whatever will happen now?

<br>

## SCENE 3
The kitchen in Lady Olivia's house

| Sir Toby |
| Sir Andrew |
| Clown |
| Maria |
| Malvolio |

[*Sir Toby and Sir Andrew come in*]

**Sir Toby** You're up early, Sir Andrew.

**Sir Andrew** I'd call it late.

**Sir Toby** No, you're wrong. If you're up after midnight it's early. By the way, old chap, do you think it's true that we're all made of atoms?

**Sir Andrew** [*Thoughtfully*] Well, that's what they say, but I think we're made of food and drink.

**Sir Toby** There's an intellectual for you! Maria, bring some wine!

**Sir Andrew** Ah! Here comes the fool.

[*The Clown comes in and puts his arms around their shoulders and his head between their heads*]

**Clown** We're three of a kind now.

**Sir Toby** [*To the Clown*] Welcome, ass! Give us a song.

**Sir Andrew** Yes, the fool's got a fine foghorn! [*To the Clown*] By the way, you were in good form last night, discussing Eisenstein and his relatives and astrology and aerobics. I was so impressed I sent you 50p so you could take your girl out. Did you get it?

**Clown** Oh yes, my dear Sir Andrew, I found a pocket for your pathetic present. For although Malvolio's nose isn't quite long enough to be a broomstick, my lady is very pretty, and the Rose and Crown is teetotal. At least north of the Trent.

**Sir Andrew** Oh, what wit! You are brilliant, sir!

**Sir Toby** Here's some money for you. Come on, sing us a song.

**Clown** Would you like a love song or a party song?

**Sir Toby** A love song, a love song!

**Sir Andrew** That's right. I don't like politics.

**Clown** [*Sings\**]    Fair lady, where are you going?
Oh wait! your true love is coming,
Singing to you.
Stay with me, my pretty darling,
We'll kiss at our journey's ending,
As lovers always do.

**Sir Andrew** That was lovely!

**Sir Toby** Good — go on!

**Clown** [*Sings\**]    Let's love and play and be happy today,
Tomorrow love may fly away,
We do not know.
We're young, so why are we waiting?
Come kiss me, my pretty darling,
Youth will soon go.

**Sir Andrew** His voice is like honey.

**Sir Toby** Yes, it's a bit sticky.

**Sir Andrew** I think it's stinky *and* sweet.

**Sir Toby** [*He sniffs*] It gets up my nose! Now let's all sing, and blow the roof off.

**Sir Andrew** Yes, let's sing "Hold your tongue, fool".

**Clown** Then I'll have to call you a fool, Sir Andrew.

**Sir Andrew** It won't be the first time. [*To the Clown*] You start.

**Clown** I can't start if I'm holding my tongue.

**Sir Andrew** That's a good one! Come on, begin.

**Together** [*As a round.\* The Clown starts*]
Hold your tongue, fool. Hold your tongue, fool.
No, I won't. No, I won't.
It's too slimy. It's too slimy.

[*Maria comes in*]

**Maria** What a horrible noise! I warn you, my lady has told Malvolio to throw you out.

**Sir Toby** My lady is a poker face, Malvolio's a raving bolero and [*he sings*] "We three kings of Orient are..." Anyway, I'm my lady's uncle!

**Clown** [*To Sir Andrew*] He's playing the fool really well tonight.

**Sir Andrew** Yes, he does it very nicely when he wants to, but I do it quite naturally.

**Sir Toby** [*Sings\*\**] "On the twelfth day of Christmas..."

---

\*  For tune see page 42
\*\* For tune see page 43

12

**Maria** [*She sees Malvolio coming and interrupts Sir Toby*] For God's sake be quiet!

[*Malvolio comes in*]

**Malvolio** Gentlemen, are you mad? Have you no respect for my lady, treating her house like a pub? Do you know what the time is?

**Sir Toby** Of course we do, we sing in time. Buzz off!

**Malvolio** Sir Toby, I'll be blunt with you. My lady's had enough of you and your nonsense. You may be her cousin, but unless you behave yourself she's ready to say goodbye.

**Sir Toby** [*Sings\* to Maria*] "Goodbye, goodbye my dear."

**Maria** Oh no, Sir Toby.

**Clown** [*Sings\* pointing at Sir Toby*] "This man will die, I fear."

**Sir Toby** Me? I'll never die.

**Malvolio** Really?

**Sir Toby** You're only a servant, you stupid steward. Do you think that because you're such a goody-goody nobody else can have fun? Go and polish your buttons! [*To Maria*] Let's have some more wine.

**Malvolio** Miss Mary, if you had any respect for my lady you would not allow this. I shall report it to her at once. [*He goes out*]

**Maria** [*Shouting after him*] Go and shake your ears, you silly ass!

**Sir Andrew** Hey, listen, I've got an idea! Why don't we challenge him to a duel and then not turn up? That'd make a fool of him.

**Sir Toby** Yes, good idea. I'll take your challenge to him.

**Maria** Not just now, Sir Toby. My lady is a bit upset, after seeing the Count's young man today. You just leave Mr. Malvolio to me; I'll make him look silly.

**Sir Toby** Come on, tell us about him.

**Maria** Well, sometimes he acts all pious—

**Sir Andrew** Oh, I'll hit him for that.

**Sir Toby** What? For being pious? Why?

**Sir Andrew** I don't know why, but I will.

**Maria** Pious indeed! He's nothing but a pompous conceited old fool who thinks he impresses everyone with all those long words he uses. He thinks *everyone* likes him — and that's how I'll catch him!

**Sir Toby** Why? What will you do?

**Maria** My handwriting is very like my lady's, so I'll make up a letter and leave it where he's sure to find it. He'll think it's for *him*.

**Sir Toby** I smell a good plot! He'll think the letter is from my niece, and that she's in love with him!

\* For tune see page 43

**Maria** That's right!

**Sir Andrew** This should be fun!

**Maria** I'll make sure that you're all there when he finds the letter. Good night. [*She goes out*]

**Sir Toby** [*Calling after her*] Good night, Queen of the Amazons!

**Sir Andrew** Quite a woman, eh?

**Sir Toby** Oh, she's smart! *And* she loves me.

**Sir Andrew** Somebody loved *me* once...

**Sir Toby** [*Yawning*] Let's go to bed. By the way, you'll need some more money.

**Sir Andrew** Look here, I'll have lost an awful lot of money if I don't get your niece.

**Sir Toby** Go on, send for the money. You'll get her in the end. Let's go and have a drink. It's too late for bed now. Come on, knight.

<br>

SCENE 4

A room in the Duke's palace

| Duke |
| Curio |
| Viola |
| Clown |
| (Attendants) |
| (Musicians) |

[*The Duke, Curio, Viola, Attendants and Musicians come in*]

**Duke** [*To the Musicians*] Music, please. [*The music starts*] Good morning friends. [*After a short while he holds up his hand and the music stops*] Cesario, I would like to hear that song we heard last night, the old one. It calmed my heart.

**Curio** Feste the jester sang it, my lord, but he's not here.

**Duke** Find him, and play the tune until he comes. [*Curio goes out. The Musicians play the tune softly while the Duke talks to Viola*] Come here, Cesario. If you should ever fall in love, my boy, remember me. All true lovers are like me, we think only of our love. We care for nothing else. [*Pause*] Do you like this tune?

**Viola** Yes, it touches my heart.

**Duke** You sound as if you are in love yourself. Are you?

**Viola** Yes, my lord, a little.

**Duke** What is she like?

**Viola** She's rather like you, my lord.

**Duke** How old is she?

**Viola** About your age.

14

**Duke** Then she's too ugly and too old. The wife should be younger than the husband, so that she remains attractive to him. I'm afraid that we men are more fickle than women.

**Viola** Yes, that's true, my lord.

[*Curio comes in with the Clown*]

**Duke** Fellow, sing that song we had last night.

**Clown** [*Sings**]        Prepare my grave ——

**Duke** [*Interrupting*] Listen, Cesario, an old love song.

**Clown** Are you ready, sir?

**Duke** Yes.

**Clown** [*Sings*]        Prepare my grave,
                      And let me rest;
                      My heart is sad,
                      And I long for death.

                      No friend must come
                      With flowers, to mourn;
                      No lover must weep
                      At my lonely tomb.

**Duke** [*Holding out a purse*] Here is your pay.

**Clown** [*He doesn't take the purse*] But I've been enjoying myself, sir.

**Duke** Then I'll pay you for enjoying yourself. [*He throws him the purse*]

**Clown** Yes, fun has to be paid for sooner or later.

**Duke** Now leave me, please.

**Clown** Thank you, Your Melancholy. Goodbye. [*He goes out*]

**Duke** [*To Curio and the others*] Please leave us. [*They go out*] Cesario, go to that cruel lady once more. Tell her I love her for her beauty and not for her fortune.

**Viola** But if she cannot love you, sir?

**Duke** [*Impatiently*] That's no answer.

**Viola** Suppose a woman loved you as much as you love the Lady Olivia. If you told her you could not love her, she would have had her answer.

**Duke** But women cannot love so well as men.

**Viola** We men may say our love is greater, but I know...[*She hesitates*]

**Duke** Yes?

**Viola** ...just how great a woman's love can be. My father had a daughter who loved a man—just as I, if I were a woman, might love your lordship. She never spoke of her love, but grew pale and thin, smiling in spite of her sorrow. Isn't that great love?

**Duke** Did your sister die of love?

* For tune see page 43

15

**Viola** I am all my father's daughters, and all his sons too, yet I do not know... Sir, shall I go to this lady?

**Duke** That's right, my boy. Give her this jewel, and tell her she *cannot* refuse me.


SCENE 5

Lady Olivia's Garden

| Sir Toby |
| Fabian |
| Maria |
| Malvolio |
| Sir Andrew |

[*Sir Toby and Sir Andrew come in followed by Fabian*]

**Sir Toby** Come along, Mr. Fabian.

**Fabian** Coming! I wouldn't miss this bit of fun for anything.

**Sir Toby** You want the sneaky rascal to look a fool, don't you?

**Fabian** You bet! He once got me into trouble over some bear-baiting.

**Sir Toby** We'll teach him a lesson—won't we, Sir Andrew? Aha! Here comes my little jewel.

[*Maria comes in*]

**Maria** Quick! Get behind that tree, Malvolio's coming. I've just seen him out there in the sun, posing in front of his own shadow! He's been doing it for the last half hour. Hurry up, hide! This letter will make an absolute idiot of him. [*They hide behind a tree. Maria puts a letter on the ground*] There you are: you're the bait—and here comes the fish! [*She goes out*]

[*Malvolio comes in*]

**Malvolio** [*To himself*] Just luck, that's all it is. I remember my lady once said to me, "Malvolio, if ever I fall in love, it will be with someone like you." And I've noticed how much better she treats me than the rest of them.

**Sir Toby** The conceited rascal!

**Fabian** Look at him—strutting about like a peacock.

**Sir Andrew** I could hit him!

**Sir Toby** Sh!

**Malvolio** "Count" Malvolio... "Count" Malvolio...

**Sir Toby** Rascal!

**Sir Andrew** Shoot him! Shoot him!

**Sir Toby** Sh!

**Malvolio** It has happened before. Ladies have been known to marry gamekeepers.

**Sir Andrew** By Lady Chatterley!

16

**Malvolio** Just imagine it! I've been married to her for about three months. I'm in my embroidered dressing gown, sitting in state—I've left Olivia sleeping. I call my officers, and look round importantly. Then I send for my relation, Toby ——

**Sir Toby** What the devil?

**Fabian** Sh! Be quiet!

**Malvolio** Seven of my men go out to get him. I wait, frowning a little, playing with my watch and - er - well, some rich jewel. Toby comes in, bowing very low——

**Sir Toby** The fellow isn't fit to live!

**Fabian** For God's sake be quiet!

**Malvolio** I hold out my hand, like this. I frown — I mustn't be too friendly — and say, "Cousin Toby, fortune has given me your niece, therefore I have the right to say——"

**Sir Toby** What's all this?

**Malvolio** "—don't get drunk again!"

**Sir Toby** You lousy—!

**Fabian** Shut up, or you'll spoil it all.

**Malvolio** "Besides, you waste your valuable time with a stupid knight—"

**Sir Andrew** I bet that's me.

**Malvolio** "—named Sir Andrew."

**Sir Andrew** I told you so. Everyone calls me stupid.

**Malvolio** [*He sees the letter*] Hullo! What's this?

**Fabian** The fish has seen the bait.

**Sir Toby** Please God, make him read it out loud!

**Malvolio** [*He picks up the letter*] Good heavens! This is my lady's writing. [*He reads*] "To my unknown loved one, greetings." That's exactly how *she* writes. And here's my lady's seal. It's *from* her, but who is it *to*?

**Fabian** Now he's swallowing the bait.

**Malvolio** [*He reads*]      "I may command the man I love
                              But cannot tell his name;
                              For my sad heart and tearful cheeks
                              MOAI'S to blame."
"MOAI." What can that mean? Let me think...

**Fabian** There's a hook in it all right.

**Sir Toby** And he'll swallow the lot!

**Malvolio** "I may command the man I love." Well, she may command *me*, I'm her servant. That's quite clear. But what about the alphabetical part? If only I could see myself in that. M..O..A..I....

**Sir Toby** It's a bit difficult for him.

**Fabian** He'll sniff it out.

**Malvolio** M, Malvolio. Aha! My name starts with M. A should come next, but it says O. That's odd. And I's at the end....

**Fabian** If you had an eye at your back end you might see trouble behind you.

**Malvolio** These letters are certainly all in my name.... Oh! Here's some prose. [*He reads*]
"I am greater than you are, but you may become great too. Take this chance! Be bold! Throw off your old ways. Quarrel with my cousin. Be rude to the servants. Be an authority on world affairs. Get people to notice you. Remember who admired your yellow stockings and your cross-gartering. Be master of your fate, or remain a servant for ever. Farewell."
[*Excitedly*] This is all as clear as daylight! I *will* be bold. I *will* be rude to Sir Toby. I'll read *The Times*. I'll make people notice me. She praised my yellow stockings and cross-gartering only the other day. This shows she really loves me, and that I'm not making it up. Oh how lucky I am...! But here's a P.S. [*He reads*]
"You must know who I am. If you love me, smile when you are with me. You look so sweet when you smile, my dear."
Oh yes, I will smile. I will do it all. [*He goes out*]

**Fabian** I wouldn't sell my share in this trick for a million pounds!

**Sir Toby** I could marry the woman for it.

**Sir Andrew** Me too!

**Sir Toby** And the only dowry I'd want would be another joke like this.

**Sir Andrew** Same here!

**Fabian** Here comes our fisherwoman.

[*Maria comes in again*]

**Sir Toby** Do you want me for your slave?

**Sir Andrew** And me?

**Maria** Is it really working?

**Sir Toby** Like whisky!

**Maria** Well, if you want to see the best part of the joke you must watch him when he goes to see my lady next. She hates yellow, she detests cross-gartering, and his smiles will annoy her so much that he'll really get into trouble. Come with me!

**Sir Toby** To the ends of the earth!

**Sir Andrew** Me too!

18

# ACT 3

## SCENE 1
### Lady Olivia's garden

[*The* **Clown** *is playing on a drum.* **Viola** *comes in*]

| |
|---|
| Viola |
| Clown |
| Sir Toby |
| Sir Andrew |
| Olivia |
| (Maria) |

**Viola** Hullo! Do you live by playing the drum?

**Clown** No, sir. I live by the church.

**Viola** Are you a priest?

**Clown** No. But my house is near the church.

**Viola** You might as well stand beside the church and then say the church is near you.

**Clown** Well, you can do anything with words these days.

**Viola** Aren't you the Lady Olivia's fool?

**Clown** No, sir. She won't have one of those till she's married. I'm just her word twister.

**Viola** Didn't I see you at Count Orsino's the other day?

**Clown** Oh, fools are like the sun, they shine everywhere. Didn't *I* see *you* at the Count's, my learned friend?

**Viola** That's enough from you! But wait, here's some money.[*She gives him a coin*]

**Clown** Thank you, sir. May God send you a beard when he has one to spare!

**Viola** Yes, I'd give anything to have one [*to the audience*] though not on *my* chin. [*To the* **Clown**] Is your lady in?

**Clown** [*Pointing to the coin*] This needs a wife, sir.

**Viola** So they'll multiply, eh? That's a good bit of begging. [*She gives him another coin*]

**Clown** Thank you, sir.[*He winks*] I'll be your go-between. I'll tell my lady you have come—or shall I *inform* her of your *arrival*? [*He goes out*]

**Viola** I'd never realised how bright you have to be to play the fool well. To make fun of people, you really have to know quite a lot about them. It's a serious business being a jester.

[**Sir Toby** *and* **Sir Andrew** *come in*]

19

**Sir Toby** Greetings, gentleman.

**Viola** Greetings, sir.

**Sir Andrew** *Bonjour, monsieur.*

**Viola** [*Bowing*] *Monsieur.*

**Sir Toby** Do you want to do business with my niece?

**Viola** Yes, sir. She is my - er - customer.

**Sir Toby** Taste your legs, sir.

**Viola** I'm afraid my legs stand under me better than I under-stand you.

**Sir Toby** I mean, walk in, sir.

**Viola** Thank you. [*She starts off*] But here she is! [*Olivia and Maria come in*] Lovely lady, may heaven rain sweet perfumes on you!

**Sir Andrew** "Rain sweet perfumes." Gosh, that's good! I must remember to use it myself sometime.

**Olivia** [*To Sir Toby, Sir Andrew and Maria*] Leave us! [*They go out*] Give me your hand. What is your name?

**Viola** Cesario is your servant's name, fair princess.

**Olivia** But you are Count Orsino's servant.

**Viola** And he is your servant, so I—

**Olivia** [*Interrupting*] I wish the Count would forget about me.

**Viola** But I have come to plead for him.

**Olivia** Please don't talk about him. [*Softly*] It is *you* I want to hear from.

**Viola** Dear lady—

**Olivia** Please listen! After your last visit here, when you cast your spell on me, I sent you a ring. It was wrong of me, I know...But I've said enough. You must know what I mean. I am at your mercy. [*Pause*] Have you nothing to say?

**Viola** I am sorry for you.

**Olivia** Pity may lead to love.

**Viola** But we often pity our *enemies.*

**Olivia** Well then, there's no more to be said! And yet I don't regret having fallen in love with you....[*A clock strikes*] But I mustn't waste any more time. Don't worry, young man, you are safe from me. [*She sighs*] And yet I envy your future wife; she will get a fine husband. [*Sharply*] Now go! Try your luck somewhere else.

**Viola** So you have no message for my master?

**Olivia** Wait! What do you think of me?

**Viola** That you do not know yourself.

**Olivia** I could say the same of you.

**Viola** You are right, I am *not* what I seem.

**Olivia** I know what I want you to be.

**Viola** [*Angrily*] Would that be an improvement, madam?

**Olivia** [*To herself*] How handsome he looks when he's angry! [*To Viola*] Oh Cesario, I love you so much that I cannot hide my feelings any longer. Please don't turn against me for speaking so openly to you. Surely love that is freely given is better than love that has to be asked for?

**Viola** Madam, my heart can never belong to any woman. And I will never come again to plead for my master. Goodbye.

**Olivia** Oh, but you must come again. You may yet learn to love me.


SCENE 2

The kitchen in Lady Olivia's house


[*Sir Toby, Sir Andrew and Fabian come in*]

| Sir Andrew |
|---|
| Sir Toby |
| Fabian |
| Maria |

**Sir Andrew** No, I won't! I won't stay another minute.

**Sir Toby** But why, dear poison, why?

**Fabian** Go on, tell us why.

**Sir Andrew** Well, I saw your niece being nicer to the Count's servant than she's ever been to me. I saw it in the orchard.

**Sir Toby** Did *she* see *you*, old boy?

**Sir Andrew** As plainly as I see you now.

**Fabian** That shows she loves you.

**Sir Andrew** Nonsense! You're making fun of me.

**Fabian** I'll prove it. [*He winks at Sir Toby*] She did it to annoy you, to - er - wake you up. You should have gone along, cracked a few good jokes, and made the young man look silly. Now you've missed your chance, and my lady won't take any notice of you — unless you do something brave, or clever.

**Sir Andrew** I'm not very clever, so I suppose I'd better do something b-b-brave.

**Sir Toby** That's right. You must challenge the youth to a duel, and wound him in eleven places. My niece will notice, and there you are! No woman can resist a brave man.

**Fabian** It's the only way, Sir Andrew.

**Sir Andrew** W-will either of you take a challenge to him for me?

**Sir Toby** You just go and write it! Threaten him! Cover the page with lies! Put acid in your ink if you have to. Go on, get to work.

**Sir Andrew** Where will I find you?

21

**Sir Toby** Don't worry, we'll come and fetch you. Off you go! [*Sir Andrew goes out*]

**Fabian** He's a dear fellow, Sir Toby.

**Sir Toby** I'm a bit dear for him, my boy. I've already cost him twenty thousand pounds or so.

**Fabian** His letter will be a laugh. But you won't deliver it, will you?

**Sir Toby** Of course I will! *And* I'll make the youth answer. But wild horses won't get these two together. Sir Andrew hasn't got a drop of real blood in him.

**Fabian** And the youth doesn't look exactly fierce.

[*Maria is heard laughing off stage*]

**Sir Toby** Aha! Here comes my little dickybird.

[*Maria comes in laughing*]

**Maria** If you want a good laugh, come with me! Malvolio's swallowed the lot. He's in yellow stockings.

**Sir Toby** And cross-gartered?

**Maria** Yes, like an old schoolmaster! He's doing everything the letter said. He's grinning all over his face — I'm sure my lady will hit him. *And* he'll love it. He'll just smile!

**Sir Toby** Come on, take us to him!


SCENE 3

A street in the city

[*Sebastian and Antonio come in*]

> Sebastian
> Antonio

**Sebastian** Antonio, you really shouldn't have bothered to come.

**Antonio** I was worried about what might happen to you. You're a stranger here.

**Sebastian** I can never thank you enough for your kindness. [*Cheerfully*] What shall we do now? See the sights of the town?

**Antonio** We'll do that tomorrow, sir. We ought to find lodgings now.

**Sebastian** I'm not tired and it's still quite early. Let's see the town.

**Antonio** Excuse me, sir, but I am too well known here to be safe. I once fought against the Count's navy.

**Sebastian** And I suppose you killed many of his men?

**Antonio** It was not that. The fact is that I am the only man from my city who never paid back what he took in battle.

22

**Sebastian** Then you mustn't be seen here.

**Antonio** That's right, sir. Here is my purse. We will stay at the Elephant hotel in the southern suburbs. You go and look round the town, and we'll meet there later.

**Sebastian** But why the money?

**Antonio** You may find some souvenir you want to buy. I'll see you at the Elephant.

**Sebastian** All right, I won't forget. [*They go out opposite ways*]

SCENE 4

Lady Olivia's garden

[*Olivia comes in with Maria*]

| Olivia | Sir Andrew |
|--------|-----------|
| Maria | Viola |
| Malvolio | Antonio |
| Attendant | 1st Police |
| Sir Toby | 2nd Police |
| Fabian | |

**Olivia** [*To herself*] I have sent for the youth. What shall I give him, if he comes? [*To Maria*] Where is Malvolio? [*Maria goes and looks off stage*] Malvolio suits my mood; he is so solemn and sensible.

**Maria** He's coming, madam, but I'm afraid there's something very wrong with him. He's grinning all over his face. He doesn't look at all safe, madam. I'm sure he's mad.

**Olivia** Tell him to come here. [*Maria goes out*] I'm just as mad as he is, but mine is a sad madness. [*Maria comes in again with Malvolio, who is smiling and wearing yellow stockings with cross-gartering*] Well, Malvolio?

**Malvolio** Aha, my sweet lady!

**Olivia** What are you smiling for? This is a sad occasion.

**Malvolio** Sad, my lady? I could be sad, because this cross-gartering is rather bad for my circulation. But what does that matter, if it pleases a *certain person*. [*He looks lovingly at Olivia, and kisses his hand*]

**Olivia** What's the matter with you?

**Malvolio** I have received it, and I recognised the sweet writing. I will do it all!

**Olivia** Are you all right, Malvolio? Ought you to go to bed?

**Malvolio** To bed! With pleasure, my dear!

**Olivia** Good heavens! Why are you smiling and kissing your hand all the time?

**Maria** How are you, Malvolio?

**Malvolio** [*To Maria*] I am at your service, worm!

**Maria** What's all this showing off for? *And* in front of my lady.

23

**Malvolio** [*To Olivia*] "You may become great too."

**Olivia** What's this?

**Malvolio** "Take this chance."

**Olivia** Poor fellow!

**Malvolio** "Remember who admired your yellow stockings."

**Olivia** My yellow stockings? The man's mad.

[*An Attendant comes in*]

**Attendant** [*To Olivia*] Madam, I have persuaded Count Orsino's young gentleman to come back. He is waiting to see you.

**Olivia** I'll come. [*The Attendant goes out*] Maria, make sure this fellow is looked after, I'd hate to lose him. And fetch my cousin Toby. [*Olivia and Maria go out opposite ways*]

**Malvolio** Aha! This fits in with the letter. She's sending for Sir Toby so that I can be rude to him. You see, she told me in her letter just how to behave towards everyone. Oh, I've caught her! Though I admit it was partly luck. And she called me "fellow" just now. That's very friendly.

[*Maria comes in again with Sir Toby and Fabian*]

**Sir Toby** Where is he? The devil himself won't stop me speaking to him.

**Fabian** Here he is. [*To Malvolio*] How are you, sir? [*Malvolio does not reply*] How are you, man?

**Malvolio** Go away! Leave me alone!

**Maria** There you are, it's the devil speaking. Sir Toby, my lady wants you to look after him.

**Malvolio** Does she now?

**Sir Toby** [*To Maria and Fabian*] Sh! We must be gentle. Let me try. [*He slaps Malvolio on the back*] How are you, Malvolio? Don't give in to the devil.

**Malvolio** Do you know what you are saying?

**Maria** [*Kneeling down*] Oh-h-h! I pray he's not bewitched. My lady couldn't bear to lose him.

**Malvolio** Hullo, mistress!

**Maria** [*She pretends to be frightened*] Oh-h-h-h!

**Sir Toby** [*To Maria*] Please be quiet, you're upsetting him. Leave him to me.

**Fabian** Yes, gently does it.

**Sir Toby** [*Heartily*] Well, how are you, old cock?

**Maria** Get him to say his prayers, Sir Toby.

**Malvolio** My prayers, wretch?

**Maria** Oh dear! Oh dear! He won't let religion help him. [*She stands up*]

**Malvolio** Go and hang yourselves, all of you! I am not made of the same cheap stuff as you are. You'll find out more later. [*He goes out*]

**Sir Toby** This is incredible!

**Fabian** If it had been acted on a stage, I wouldn't have believed it.

**Maria** Let's follow him.

**Sir Toby** Look, why don't we tie him up and put him in a dark room? My niece is convinced he's mad, so we can have fun teasing and tormenting him until we're bored.

[*Sir Andrew comes in*]

**Fabian** [*To Sir Toby and Maria*] Here's some more fun.

**Sir Andrew** Here's the challenge. There's plenty of pepper in it.

**Fabian** Hot stuff, eh?

**Sir Toby** Let's have it. [*He takes the letter and reads*] "Youth: whatever you are, you're a rascal!"

**Fabian** Very brave!

**Sir Toby** "Don't ask why I say this. I won't tell you."

**Fabian** That will keep him on the right side of the law.

**Sir Toby** "I saw the Lady Olivia treat you nicely. You're a liar, but that's not what I challenge you for."

**Fabian** He's lying low!

**Sir Toby** "I will ambush you on your way home. If you kill me you are a villain. Yours in frightful friendship, Andrew Aguecheek." This should give the youth a heart attack! I'll give it to him.

**Maria** [*Pointing off stage*] Look, now's your chance! He's talking to my lady, and he'll be leaving soon.

**Sir Toby** [*To Sir Andrew*] Go and wait for him at the corner of the orchard. When you see him, draw your sword and swear horribly. That'll make him think you're brave. Off you go!

**Sir Andrew** You won't beat *me* at swearing. [*He goes out*]

**Sir Toby** [*He looks at the letter again*] I can't deliver this. The young gentleman seems to be intelligent, and he'll see it's from a blockhead. But I *will* deliver the challenge verbally, and I'll make the youth so scared of Sir Andrew that they'll die of fright when they see each other.

**Fabian** [*He sees Olivia and Viola coming*] Ah, here they come. Let's wait over there, and follow the youth when he leaves her.

**Sir Toby** I'll think up a horrid message for a challenge. [*Sir Toby, Fabian and Maria go out*]

[*Olivia and Viola come in the other side*]

**Olivia** I know I am wrong to open my heart to you, but I cannot help it.

**Viola** That's exactly how my master feels about you.

**Olivia** [*Giving her a locket*] Here is my portrait. I want you to wear it. And please come again tomorrow. [*Pause*] What else can I give you?

**Viola** Your love for my master.

**Olivia** But that's impossible, I have given it to you.

**Viola** I will let you have it back.

**Olivia** [*She sighs*] Ah well! Goodbye. But you will come again tomorrow?
[*She goes out*]
[*Sir Toby and Fabian come in again*]

**Sir Toby** Greetings, sir.

**Viola** And to you, sir.

**Sir Toby** You must defend yourself, sir. I don't know what you've done to him, but your enemy is in a terrible temper. He's after your blood. Come on, draw your sword.

**Viola** You must have made a mistake, sir. I haven't got any enemies.

**Sir Toby** That's what you think!

**Viola** But who is he?

**Sir Toby** He's only a New Year's knight, but he's *terribly* brave. He's already killed three people, and he's out to get you!

**Viola** I'll go back into the house and ask for help. I'm no fighter. I think this man must have *invented* a quarrel. [*She starts to go*]

**Sir Toby** [*Stopping her*] Oh no, you don't! He's got a real grievance against you. You've got to face him. Draw your sword, sir, or else admit you're a coward.

**Viola** What strange, rude behaviour! Please ask the knight what I've done wrong. Whatever it is, I certainly didn't mean it.

**Sir Toby** All right. [*To Fabian*] Fabian, you stay with this gentleman till I get back. [*He goes out*]

**Viola** Excuse me, sir, but do you know what all this is about?

**Fabian** All I know is that the knight is angry with you, and he's out for your blood.

**Viola** What sort of a person is he?

**Fabian** He's not much to look at, but he's the terror of the town. But if you come with me, I'll try to make you friends. [*They move to one side*]

**Viola** Oh, thank you. I'm scared, and I don't care who knows it.

[*Sir Toby and Sir Andrew come in and stand at the other side*]

**Sir Toby** The youth's an absolute devil, and he's a wonder with his sword.

**Sir Andrew** Look here, Sir Toby, I've had enough.

**Sir Toby** It's too late now. Fabian can hardly hold him back.

**Sir Andrew** If only I'd known, I wouldn't have challenged him. Look, I'll give him my horse, Grey Capilet, if he'll call it off.

**Sir Toby** Mmm... I'll see what I can do. Wait here. [*To himself*] I'll manage your horse as well as I manage you. [*Sir Toby goes to the middle of the stage and calls Fabian*] Here! [*Fabian goes to him, and Sir Toby whispers*] He'll give his horse if he can get out of the quarrel. I've persuaded him the youth's a devil.

**Fabian** [*Whispers*] And the boy's just as scared of Sir Andrew.

**Sir Toby** [*He goes and speaks to Viola*] I'm afraid there's no way out, sir. The knight feels he must keep his word. But he's not as angry as he was, and he has promised not to hurt you. Come on, draw your sword.

**Viola** [*To herself*] God help me! It won't take much to show I'm not a man.

**Sir Toby** [*He goes and speaks to Sir Andrew*] Come on, Sir Andrew! There's no way out. He's determined to fight you, but he's promised not to hurt you.

**Sir Andrew** I h-hope he k-keeps his promise. [*Sir Andrew and Viola go slowly towards each other and start fighting feebly*]

[*Antonio comes in*]

**Antonio** [*To Viola*] Put your sowrd away. [*To Sir Andrew*] I will take this young gentleman's place.

**Sir Toby** You! Who are *you*?

**Antonio** [*Drawing his sword*] A faithful friend, who sticks to his word.

**Sir Toby** [*Drawing his sword*] I'll stick you!

**Fabian** [*Holding Sir Toby and pointing off stage*] Stop, Sir Toby! Here come the police.

**Sir Toby** [*To Antonio*] I'll see you later.

**Viola** [*To Sir Andrew*] Put your sword away.

**Sir Andrew** [*Gratefully*] Certainly, certainly! And I'll give you what I promised. He's a good horse. [*Viola looks amazed*]

[*Two Policemen come in*]

**1st Policeman** [*Pointing to Antonio*] That's the man. Arrest him!

**2nd Policeman** I arrest you on Count Orsino's orders.

**Antonio** [*To the 1st Policeman*] You have made a mistake.

**1st Policeman** No, sir. I recognise you, even though you aren't in uniform. [*To the 2nd Policeman*] Take him away! He knows I know him.

**Antonio** Very well. [*To Viola*] This is because I came out to look for you. But it can't be helped, I must go. How will you manage now? Especially as I must ask you for my purse. [*Pause*] What's the matter?

**2nd Policeman** Come, sir.

**Antonio** [*To Viola*] I must ask you for some of that money.

**Viola** What money? I don't understand. But you have been very kind to me, so [*taking out her purse*] I'll share what little I have with you.

**Antonio** But you know me! How can you treat me like this after all I have done for you?

**Viola** I don't know you, I have never seen you before. But since I hate ingratitude more than——

**Antonio** My God!

**2nd Policeman** Please come, sir.

**Antonio** Just a moment, I've got something to say first. I saved this young man from death, and then grew to like and admire him.

**1st Policeman** That's nothing to do with us. Come along!

**Antonio** You vile creature! Oh Sebastian, you may look like a god, but you have feet of clay!

**1st Policeman** [*To 2nd Policeman*] The fellow's going mad. [*To Antonio*] Come, sir.

**Antonio** All right, I'll come. [*The Policemen take him out*]

**Viola** [*To herself*] He really seems to think he knows me. Have I been mistaken for my brother?

**Sir Toby** Come knight, come Fabian. [*He puts his arms round their shoulders and leads them to the back of the stage*] Have you heard the one about...?

**Viola** [*To herself*] He said "Sebastian". I look like him, and I'm dressed like him. Can my brother be alive after all? [*She goes out*]

**Sir Toby** What a false friend! And he's a coward.

**Fabian** Yes! A true, practising coward.

**Sir Andrew** I'll go and hit him.

**Sir Toby** That's right! Give him a good thrashing, but don't use your sword.

**Sir Andrew** [*As he runs out*] I'll get him!

**Fabian** Come on. Let's go and see what happens.

**Sir Toby** Nothing at all, I'll bet.

# ACT 4

## SCENE 1

### A street near Lady Olivia's house

| Clown |
|---|
| Sebastian |
| Sir Andrew |
| Sir Toby |
| (Fabian) |
| Olivia |

[*Sebastian comes in followed by the Clown*]

**Clown** I tell you I *was* sent to fetch you.

**Sebastian** Nonsense! You don't know me.

**Clown** [*Holding his nose*] You'll be telling me next that this isn't my nose, and that you're not Cesario.

**Sebastian** Well, I'm not. Go and play the buffoon somewhere else.

**Clown** "Play the buffoon" eh? My goodness, where did you pick that up? Come on now, do be sensible. Shall I tell my lady you are coming?

**Sebastian** Look, here's some money for you. Now go, before I beat you.

[*Sir Andrew comes in*]

**Sir Andrew** [*To Sebastian*] Ah, there you are again. Take that! [*He punches Sebastian*]

**Sebastian** And you take that! [*He punches Sir Andrew*] Is *everyone* mad? [*He draws his sword and beats Sir Andrew with it*]

[*Sir Toby and Fabian come in*]

**Sir Toby** [*Holding Sebastian's sword arm*] Stop, sir!

**Clown** I'll go and tell my lady about this. I wouldn't be in your shoes for anything. [*He goes out*]

**Sir Toby** [*To Sebastian*] Come sir, stop!

**Sir Andrew** [*Rubbing his head, which has been hurt*] Leave him alone, Sir Toby. I've thought of a better way of dealing with him. I'll take him to court, even though I hit him first.

29

**Sebastian** [*To Sir Toby, who is still holding him*] Let me go!

**Sir Toby** No, I won't. Put away your sword, you young devil!

**Sebastian** Get off! [*He gets away from Sir Toby*] Right. I've had enough. Do you want a fight?

**Sir Toby** Oho! What's all this? [*He draws his sword*] All right, young fellow, we'll check the colour of your blood! [*They fight*]

[*Olivia comes in*]

**Olivia** Stop, Toby! Stop, I tell you!

**Sir Toby** [*Stopping and bowing*] Madam!

**Olivia** You wretch, will you never learn to behave? [*To Sebastian*] Please do not be offended, dear Cesario. [*To Sir Toby*] Get out of my sight! [*Sir Toby, Sir Andrew and Fabian go out*] Do not be angry, dear friend. This fellow is always doing something stupid — some mischief — you must just laugh at him. Come with me.

**Sebastian** [*To himself*] What is going on? What is happening to me? Have I gone mad, or am I dreaming? If this is a dream, I hope I never wake up!

**Olivia** Please come. [*She sighs*] I wish you would do what I want!

**Sebastian** But madam, I will.


### SCENE 2
The kitchen in Lady Olivia's house

[*Maria and the Clown come in. Malvolio is just off stage. He is locked up in a dark room*]

| |
|---|
| Maria |
| Clown |
| Sir Toby |
| Malvolio (off stage) |

**Maria** Quick, put these on! [*She gives him a priest's cassock and a beard*] Pretend you are Sir Topas the curate. I'll go and fetch Sir Toby. [*She goes out*]

**Clown** [*Putting them on*] All right, I'll put them on. And it won't be the first time these things have been used to hide a few shortcomings. [*He finds that the cassock is too big for him*] Oh dear, I'm a bit too short to be a priest, and a bit too thin to be a good student. Never mind! It's just as good to be a cheerful, friendly fellow.

[*Sir Toby and Maria come in*]

**Sir Toby** [*To the Clown*] God bless you, Mr. Parson!

**Clown** [*Solemnly, imitating a priest's voice*] Good day, Sir Toby. As the old professor at Oxbridge said to the niece of King Kong, "What is, is." So I, being Mr. Parson, am Mr. Parson, For what is "is" but "is"?

**Sir Toby** Go and talk to him, Sir Topas.

**Clown** [*He goes to the side of the stage, and speaks to **Malvolio** in the priest's voice*] Peace in this prison!

**Sir Toby** [*To **Maria**] The rascal's playing his part very well.

**Malvolio** [*Off stage*] Who is that?

**Clown** [*Priest's voice*] Sir Topas the curate, who has come to visit Malvolio the lunatic.

**Malvolio** Sir Topas! Dear Sir Topas! Please go to my lady.

**Clown** [*Priest's voice*] Out, foul devil! Why do you make this man talk of nothing but ladies?

**Sir Toby** Well said, Mr. Parson!

**Malvolio** Sir Topas, I've been wronged. Please don't think I'm mad. They've left me here in the dark.

**Clown** [*Priest's voice*] Out, you naughty devil! [*To the audience*] I don't like being very rude, even to the devil. [*To **Malvolio**] Did you say "in the dark"?

**Malvolio** It's as dark as hell in here, Sir Topas.

**Clown** [*Priest's voice*] But it's as bright as night, with darkness streaming in through the shut shutters!

**Malvolio** I'm *not* mad. It *is* dark in here.

**Clown** [*Priest's voice*] This is the darkness of ignorance.

**Malvolio** I'm not mad. Test me and see.

**Clown** [*Priest's voice*] Very well. What does the Bible say about Evolution?

**Malvolio** That Darwin got it wrong.

**Clown** [*Priest's voice*] What is your opinion?

**Malvolio** I think that man is a noble creature, and I don't approve of Darwin.

**Clown** [*Priest's voice, very solemnly*] Oh, Malvolio! I'm afraid you will have to stay in the dark until you have sorted out your ancestors. Goodbye.

**Malvolio** Sir Topas! Sir Topas!

**Sir Toby** That was brilliant, Sir Topas!

**Clown** [*In his own voice*] Yes, I'm an all rounder.

**Maria** You could have done all this without the beard and cassock, fool. He can't see you.

**Sir Toby** Now go and speak to him in your own voice. We must finish this game off quickly, because I'm already in trouble with my niece. Come to my room later on. [***Sir Toby** and **Maria** go out*]

31

**Clown** [*He starts singing**]
                Tell me little bird
                How your lady is.

**Malvolio** [*Calling*] Fool...

**Clown** [*Sings*] My lady is unkind.

**Malvolio** Fool...

**Clown** [*Sings*] Why is that?

**Malvolio** Fool...

**Clown** [*Sings*] She loves another. [*He speaks*] Who's that?

**Malvolio** Dear fool, please bring me a candle and a pen and some paper.

**Clown** [*He pretends to be surprised*] It's MALVOLIO!

**Malvolio** Yes, dear fool.

**Clown** Oh dear, oh dear! How did *you* go mad?

**Malvolio** I've been wronged. I'm as sane as you are.

**Clown** As sane as I am? Then you're mad all right.

**Malvolio** They've certainly done their best to drive me mad, keeping me here shut up in the dark and sending me priests. The idiots!

**Clown** Sh! Be careful what you say, here *is* the priest. [*Priest's voice*] Malvolio, Malvolio, try to sleep and stop burbling.

**Malvolio** Sir Topas!

**Clown** [*Priest's voice*] Do not speak to him, my man. [*In his own voice*] Me, sir? Certainly not, Sir Topas. [*Priest's voice*] That's right. [*Own voice*] Yes, sir.

**Malvolio** Fool... Fool...

**Clown** But sir, I've just been told off for speaking to you.

**Malvolio** Dear fool, please bring me what I asked for. I tell you I'm as sane as anyone in Illyria.

**Clown** I wish you were, sir.

**Malvolio** Believe me, I am. Please bring me some paper and ink and a light, so that I can write to my lady. I'll pay you well.

**Clown** All right, I'll bring them. But tell me seriously: are you really mad, or just pretending?

**Malvolio** I tell you, I'm *not* mad. Please go.

**Clown** [*He sings as he goes out*]
                I will go, sir
                And be back soon...

* For tune see page 43

# SCENE 3
## Lady Olivia's garden

| |
|---|
| Sebastian |
| Olivia |
| (Priest) |

[*Sebastian comes in*]

**Sebastian** [*He speaks slowly. He is puzzled*] I can breathe...I can feel the warmth of the sun...Here is the pearl she gave me: I can feel it and see it...I may be dreaming, but I'm certainly not mad. But where is Antonio? They said at the hotel that he had gone out to look for me. I could do with his advice now. There must be some mistake, it is all so strange. [*Pause*] Is it possible that the lady is mad? But she *can't* be. She manages her servants and other business perfectly. Ah, here she comes!

[*Olivia comes in with a Priest*]

**Olivia** [*To Sebastian*] Please forgive me for being in such a hurry. If you care for me, come with me to the chapel. The priest will keep the marriage a secret until you decide to announce it, and we can leave the celebrations until then. Promise me you will be true to me, and put an end to my doubt and jealousy.

**Sebastian** I promise.

**Olivia** [*To the Priest*] Lead on, Father. May heaven bless us!

# ACT 5

## SCENE 1

The street in front of Lady Olivia's house

[*Fabian comes in with the Clown,*
*who is carrying a letter*]

**Fabian** Come on, let me see his letter.

**Clown** Will you do something for me, Fabian?

**Fabian** Anything you like.

**Clown** Then don't ask to see Malvolio's letter.

| | |
|---|---|
| Fabian | Antonio |
| Clown | Olivia |
| Duke | (Attendants) |
| Viola | Priest |
| (Curio) | Sir Andrew |
| (Attendants) | Sir Toby |
| 1st Police | Sebastian |
| (2nd Police) | Malvolio |

**Fabian** You might as well give me a present, and then ask to have it back again because you've been so generous.

[*The Duke comes in with Viola, Curio and some Attendants*]

**Duke** [*To Fabian and the Clown*] Do you belong to the Lady Olivia?

**Clown** Yes, sir. We're her property.

**Duke** Ah, I recognise you. How are you, fellow?

**Clown** I'm very well, sir, thanks to my enemies.

**Duke** Surely you mean your friends?

**Clown** No, sir. You see, my friends praise me and then make a fool of me, but my enemies tell me quite plainly that I'm a fool. So at least I learn something from my enemies.

**Duke** Well argued! I promise you won't lose by me. [*He gives him a coin*]

**Clown** What about some [*he winks*] double-dealing, sir?

**Duke** That's bad advice.

**Clown** Oh, come on, sir! Follow your feelings, and forget your principles for once.

**Duke** All right, then. [*He gives him another coin*]

**Clown** Third time lucky, sir?

**Duke** You won't fool any more out of me this time. But if you tell your lady I am here and bring her to me, you may re-awaken my generosity.

**Clown** Very good, sir. Let your purse have a little rest, and I'll wake it up later. But don't think I'm greedy. [*He runs out*]

34

[*The two* **Policemen** *bring* **Antonio** *in*]

**Viola** Here comes the man that rescued me, sir.

**Duke** I know this man's face well, though I last saw him in the heat and smoke of battle. He fought bravely then. What's the matter?

**1st Policeman** My lord, this is Antonio, who once captured the Phoenix with her cargo and fought with your nephew Titus. We found him fighting in the street.

**Viola** [*To the* **Duke**] He was helping me, my lord. He came to my rescue. But afterwards he spoke to me in a very strange way.

**Duke** Pirate and thief! How dare you come here!

**Antonio** Sir, I have never been a thief or a pirate, though I admit I am your enemy. I followed that ungrateful boy [*he points to* **Viola**] after saving him from drowning. I befriended him, and even risked coming to this town for his sake. When he was attacked, I came to his rescue. Now he pretends he doesn't know me, and says I never gave him my purse.

**Duke** When did he come to this town?

**Antonio** Today, my lord. And until today we had been together for three months.

**Duke** [*Looking off stage*] Ah, here comes my lovely lady! [*To* **Antonio**] Sir, you are talking nonsense! This youth has been with *me* for the last three months. [*To the two* **Policemen**] Take him over there. I'll deal with him later.

[*The* **Policemen** *take* **Antonio** *to one side as* **Olivia** *comes in from the opposite side with her* **Attendants**]

**Olivia** [*To the* **Duke**] What can I give you, my lord — except, of course, my love? [*She sees* **Viola**, *and speaks sternly to her*] Cesario, you have broken your promise.

**Viola** Madam?

**Duke** Gracious Olivia——

**Olivia** What have you to say, Cesario? [*To the* **Duke**] Just a moment, my lord.

**Viola** [*To* **Olivia**] My master wishes to speak, so I must be silent.

**Olivia** [*To the* **Duke**] If it's the old story, my lord, I'm sick and tired of it.

**Duke** Are you still so cruel?

**Olivia** I am still faithful.

**Duke** To ingratitude! Oh, what shall I do?

**Olivia** Please yourself.

**Duke** I am so jealous, I could kill you. And it might be a noble thing to do. Now listen! You have rejected my love, and I know who has taken my place in your heart. But I will not kill you. Instead, I will take away this young man, your darling. [*To* **Viola**] Come, boy. I'll take away the lamb that I love to spite the black heart of that dove. [*He moves away*]

35

**Viola** I would die a thousand times if it would make you happy. [*She follows him*]

**Olivia** [*Distractedly*] Where are you going, Cesario?

**Viola** After the man I love, and always will, more than I ever could a wife.

**Olivia** [*Nearly crying*] Oh, I am hated and deceived! [*To an **Attendant***] Call the priest. [*The **Attendant** goes out*]

**Duke** [*To **Viola***] Come with me.

**Olivia** But where, my lord? Cesario, husband, don't go!

**Duke** Husband?

**Olivia** Yes, husband. [*To **Viola***] Can you deny it?

**Duke** Are you her husband?

**Viola** Certainly not, my lord.

**Olivia** It must be fear that makes you behave so strangely. Come, Cesario, be yourself. [*The **Attendant** comes in with the **Priest***] Welcome, Father. Please tell these people about myself and this young man.

**Priest** I married them two hours ago. They joined hands, kissed, and promised to be true to each other.

**Duke** [*To **Viola***] You deceitful puppy! Take her, and never let me see you again!

**Viola** My lord, I never——

**Olivia** [*To **Viola***] Don't deny me, even though you are afraid.

[*Sir **Andrew** comes in holding his head*]

**Sir Andrew** A doctor! A doctor! And send one to Sir Toby.

**Olivia** What's the matter?

**Sir Andrew** He's cut my head open, and Sir Toby's too. I'd give a thousand pounds to be at home again.

**Olivia** Who has, Sir Andrew?

**Sir Andrew** The Count's gentleman, Cesario. We thought he was a coward, but he's an absolute devil.

**Duke** [*Surprised*] My gentleman Cesario?

**Sir Andrew** [*He sees **Viola***] Good lord, here he is! [ *To **Viola***] You cut my head open for nothing. It was Sir Toby who made me fight you.

**Viola** But it was you who attacked me, and for no reason at all. I never hurt you.

**Sir Andrew** [*Pointing to a cut on his head*] What's this, then? Do you think it doesn't hurt? Ah, here comes Sir Toby. If he hadn't been drunk, he'd have dealt with you properly.

[*Sir **Toby** and the **Clown** come in. Sir **Toby** is limping*]

**Duke** [*To Sir **Toby***] How are you, sir?

**Sir Toby** He's hurt me, and that's that. [*To the Clown*] Can't you find the doctor?

**Clown** Oh, he was drunk an hour ago, Sir Toby.

**Sir Toby** The useless, drunken rascal. I hate drunks.

**Olivia** Take him away. Who is responsible for this?

**Sir Andrew** I'll help you, Sir Toby. We can be bandaged together.

**Sir Toby** *You* help me, you stupid fool? [*He turns away from Sir Andrew*]

**Olivia** [*To the Clown and Fabian*] Make sure he's looked after. [*They help Sir Toby and Sir Andrew out*]

[*Sebastian comes in*]

**Sebastian** [*He bows, and speaks to Olivia*] Madam, I am sorry that I hurt your relation, but I had to defend myself. [*Pause. Olivia stares at him in surprise, and so do all the others*] I am afraid I have offended you. I am sorry, my dear.

**Duke** [*Looking from Viola to Sebastian and back again*] The same face, the same voice, the same clothes, but two people!

**Sebastian** [*He sees Antonio and goes to him*] My dear Antonio, how I have missed you!

**Antonio** Are you Sebastian?

**Sebastian** What do you mean?

**Antonio** Which of these two is Sebastian?

**Olivia** This is extraordinary!

**Sebastian** [*He sees Viola*] Is that me? I have no brother, and my only sister was drowned. Please tell me your name, and what family you come from.

**Viola** I come from Messaline. My father's name was Sebastian, and so was my brother's. He was dressed like you when he was drowned. You must be a ghost!

**Sebastian** If you were a woman, I would say "Welcome, drowned Viola!"

**Viola** My father had a mole on his forehead.

**Sebastian** [*Excitedly*] So had mine!

**Viola** And he died when Viola was thirteen.

**Sebastian** Yes, I remember that sad day.

**Viola** To prove to you that I am Viola, I'll take you to a captain's house, where I left my woman's clothes. The captain saved me, and since then I've served this Duke.

**Sebastian** [*To Olivia*] So that's how you came to make a mistake.

**Duke** [*To Olivia*] You need not worry, he is of noble birth. And perhaps I may share in this happiness. [*To Viola*] You have said over and over again that you will never love a woman as much as you love me.

**Viola** Yes, and it is true.

**Duke** Give me your hand, and let me see you in your woman's clothes.

**Viola** The captain that rescued me has got them, but he has been put in prison by Malvolio.

**Olivia** Then Malvolio must set the captain free. [*To an* **Attendant**] Fetch Malvolio! But I've just remembered, they say he's mad. [*The* **Clown** *comes in with a letter.* **Fabian** *is with him*] I quite forgot about him in my excitement. [*To the* **Clown**] How is Malvolio, my man?

**Clown** He's keeping the devil away as well as he can, madam. He has written this letter to you. I should have given it to you this morning, but you can't expect a madman's note to be in time.

**Olivia** Open it and read it.

**Clown** This will be a treat — a fool playing a madman! [*He reads as if he is mad*] "By the lord madam you have wronged me you have put me in——"

**Olivia** [*Interrupting*] Have *you* gone mad?

**Clown** No, madam. [*He points to the letter*] It's *this* that's crazy.

**Olivia** Please read it sensibly.

**Clown** I'll try, ma'am. But I have to read it as it's written.

**Olivia** [*To* **Fabian**] You read it.

**Fabian** [*He takes the letter and reads it*] "By the lord, madam, you have wronged me. You have put me in a dungeon and let your drunken cousin order me about, but I am as sane as you are. I still have your letter telling me exactly how to behave. I don't want to seem disrespectful, ma'am, but your treatment of me has forced me to speak out. Malvolio."

**Olivia** [*To the* **Clown**] Did he write this?

**Clown** Yes, madam.

**Duke** He doesn't *sound* mad.

**Olivia** [*To* **Fabian**] Bring him here, Fabian. [**Fabian** *goes out. She speaks to the* **Duke**] My lord, please accept me as a sister-in-law. We can both be married on the same day, in my house.

**Duke** Thank you, madam. You are most kind. [*To* **Viola**] You must now leave your master. But since you have served him so well, you shall be his wife! [**Fabian** *comes in with* **Malvolio**] Is this the madman?

**Olivia** Yes, my lord. [*To* **Malvolio**] Well, Malvolio?

**Malvolio** You have wronged me, madam.

**Olivia** I, Malvolio?

**Malvolio** Yes, you madam! Please look at this letter. [*He gives* **Olivia** *a letter*] You can't say it isn't from you — it is in your writing, and there's your seal. Why did you tell me to come to you wearing yellow stockings with cross-gartering, and to smile all the time? Why did you ask me to be rude to Sir Toby and to your servants? Why did you allow me to be shut up in a dark room, visited by a priest, and made a fool of by everyone? Please tell me why!

**Olivia** [*Looking at the letter*] This is not my handwriting, Malvolio, though it does look rather like it. It is Maria's writing. And now I come to think of it, it was *she* who told me you were mad, just before you came in smiling. I'm afraid they have played a mean trick on you. But don't worry, I will find out exactly who did this, and I will let *you* deal with the culprits.

**Fabian** May I speak, madam?

**Olivia** You may.

**Fabian** To prevent a quarrel at this happy time, I confess that Sir Toby and I played this trick on Malvolio, because he is so stuck up and conceited. Maria wrote the letter at Sir Toby's request, and Sir Toby has married her as a reward. We only did it for fun.

**Olivia** [*To Malvolio*] Poor Malvolio! They've really made you look a fool, haven't they?

**Clown** [*Imitating Malvolio*] "You may become great too," eh? "Sir Topas! Dear Sir Topas! Please go to my lady." Yes, I was Sir Topas, once upon a time, in one little scene. And do you remember "I'm surprised your ladyship finds the rascal amusing." Ah well, time brings its own revenge.

**Malvolio** I'll get my revenge on the lot of you. [*He goes out, shaking his fist*]

**Olivia** They've been very unkind to him.

**Duke** [*To some of his **Attendants***] Go after him and calm him. He has not told us about the captain yet, and we cannot get married until everything is settled. Come, Cesario — for I will call you Cesario until you are dressed in your own clothes and have become my wife.

[*They all go out except the **Clown***]

**Clown** [*Sings\**]

1. When I was a boy
   And a spoilt little boy,
   With a hey and a ho!
   I could do as I liked
   And it rained every day,
   With a hey and a ho!

   But when I was a lad
   I was told I was bad,
   With a hey and a ho!
   I was turned out of doors
   And it rained every day,
   With a hey and a ho!

3. Then when I got a wife
   I was sad all the time,
   With a hey and a ho!
   She took charge of my life
   And it rained every day,
   With a hey and a ho!

4. Now the world's getting old,
   And our play's at an end,
   With a hey and a ho!
   Now our play's at an end
   And it's time to go home,
   With a hey and a ho!

\* For tune see page 44

# MUSIC FOR THE SONGS

Page 12  (ACT TWO Scene 3)

CLOWN 1 Fair la - dy, where are you go - - ing? Oh
2 Let's love and play and be ha - ppy to day, To-

wait! Your true love is co - - ming,
mor - row lo - ve may fly---- a - way,

Sing - ing to you. Stay with me, my pret-ty
We---- do not know. We're young, so why are we

dar - ling, We'll kiss at our jour- ney's
wai - ting? Come kiss me, my pret - ty

end - ing, As---------- lo- vers do.
dar - ling, You- th will so- on go.

HOLD YOUR TONGUE, FOOL  Page 12  (ACT TWO Scene 3)
(Tune based on "London's Burning")

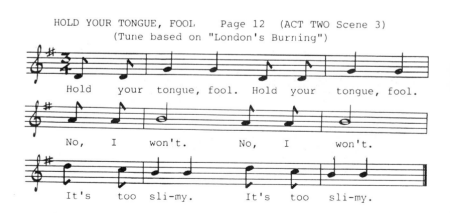

Hold your tongue, fool. Hold your tongue, fool.

No, I won't. No, I won't.

It's too sli-my. It's too sli-my.

### ON THE TWELFTH DAY OF CHRISTMAS...
Page 12 (ACT TWO Scene 3)

SIR TOBY On the twelfth day of Christ-mas...

### GOODBYE, GOODBYE MY DEAR
Page 13 (ACT TWO Scene 3)

SIR TOBY Good - bye, good - bye my dear.

CLOWN This man will die, I fear.

### PREPARE MY GRAVE
Page 15 (ACT TWO Scene 4)

CLOWN 1 Pre- pare my grave, and le - t me rest;
2 No friend must come with flo - wers, to mourn;

My heart-- is sad, and I long for death.
No lo-ver must weep at my lone - ly tomb.

### TELL ME, LITTLE BIRD...
Page 32 (ACT FOUR Scene 2)

CLOWN Tell me little bird how your la-dy is. My la- dy is un-

kind. Why is that? She lov - es an - oth - er.

# WHEN I WAS A BOY

Page 39 (ACT FIVE Scene 1)

CLOWN
1. When---- I was a boy and a spoilt lit-tle boy, With a hey and a ho! I could do as I liked And it rained every day, With a hey and a ho!
2. But when I was a lad I was told I was bad, With a hey and a ho! I was turned out of doors And it rained every day, With a hey and a ho!
3. Then when I got a wife I was sad all the time, With a hey and a ho! She took charge of my life And it rained every day, With a hey and a ho!
4. Now the world's getting old, And our play's at an end, With a hey and a ho! Now our play's at an end And it's time to go home, With a hey and a ho!